# Bonza the Monster

## and

# Sing! Sing! Sing!

Bonza

**Written by**
Kirsty Holmes

**Illustrated by**
Drue Rintoul &
Sean Chambers

# Can you say this sound and draw it with your finger?

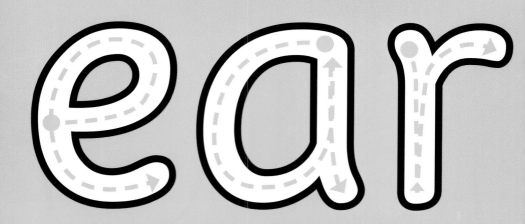

# Bonza the Monster

**Written by**
Kirsty Holmes

**Illustrated by**
Drue Rintoul

I am Bonza and I am good.

This is my hut at the top of the hill.

It is good at the top, but I need a coat.

I sit on my pink mat. I am in a good mood.

This is the wool of a yak.

A hat! It will look good with my coat!

I got a medal for being good. Look!

Look at this! Is it good?

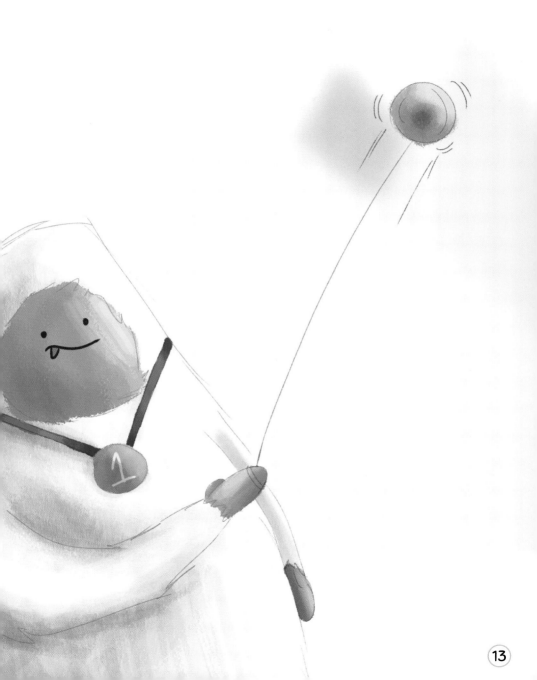

I can yell. I am good at yelling.

Did they hear me? Yes!

This is my hut. It is big and red.

Can I get you food? Can I get you a cup of coffee?

Can you say this sound and draw it with your finger?

# Sing! Sing! Sing!

**Written by**
Kirsty Holmes

**Illustrated by**
Sean Chambers

# The Sun is up. Get up, Bing!

Bing will sing a song to greet the Sun.

Look! Pong is sad.

Bing sings his song to the Sun.

"Pong, the Sun is up. I need to sing to the Sun."

"The Sun is up. I need to sing!"

Pong cannot sing. But Pong can bang!

Bang! Bang, bang, bang!

La la la la la la laaaaaaaaaa!

Bing can sing. Pong can bang.

Shush, Bing! Shush, Pong! Look!
Your hair is falling off!

The singing ends. The banging ends.

Shush!

©2021 **BookLife** Publishing Ltd.
King's Lynn, Norfolk PE30 4LS

ISBN 978-1-83927-874-7

**Bonza the Monster**
Written by Kirsty Holmes
Illustrated by Drue Rintoul
**Sing! Sing! Sing!**
Written by Kirsty Holmes
Illustrated by Sean Chambers

# An Introduction to BookLife Readers...

Our Readers have been specifically created in line with the London Institute of Education's approach to book banding and are phonetically decodable and ordered to support each phase of the Letters and Sounds document.

Each book has been created to provide the best possible reading and learning experience. Our aim is to share our love of books with children, providing both emerging readers and prolific page-turners with beautiful books that are guaranteed to provoke interest and learning, regardless of ability.

**BOOK BAND GRADED** using the Institute of Education's approach to levelling.

**PHONETICALLY DECODABLE** supporting each phase of Letters and Sounds.

**EXERCISES AND QUESTIONS** to offer reinforcement and to ascertain comprehension.

**BEAUTIFULLY ILLUSTRATED** to inspire and provoke engagement, providing a variety of styles for the reader to enjoy whilst reading through the series.

## AUTHOR INSIGHT:
## KIRSTY HOLMES

Kirsty Holmes, holder of a BA, PGCE, and an MA, was born in Norfolk, England. She has written over 60 books for BookLife Publishing, and her stories are full of imagination, creativity and fun.

**PHASE 3**

/ear/air/

This book focuses on the phonemes /ear/ and /air/ and is a yellow level 3 book band.

Additional images courtesy of Shutterstock.com. p.18 – fear1ess, romawka, yusufdemirci, Made by Marko, Maquiladora.